X

Mrs. Foothofer

150

WATCH OUT!

WATCH OUT!

Abingdon Press

NEW YORK
NASHVILLE

By NORAH SMARIDGE

Art by Susan Perl

For Benjamin
    Christopher
    Pamela
    Anton
    Timothy

SIGNS are good friends to have around!
They help to keep you safe and sound,
They tell you where to catch the bus
And where it's safe or DANGEROUS.
They mark the playground and the swings
And point to telephones and things.

Mostly they say what *not* to do—
Like poking lions in the zoo.

ONE—TWO—THREE—GO

Look to left
And look to right—
Is there anything in sight?
Bus or car
Or truck or van?
Bicycles
Or ice-cream man?

Left is empty,
So is right—
Not a single thing in sight!
Except a pup
Who does not know
The sign means ONE—TWO—THREE
And GO!

PUBLIC—PRIVATE

When you see PUBLIC, that's for *you*.
(The whole wide world is welcome, too.)
In the big public library
They'll let you borrow books, for free.
You may romp round, right up to dark,
With Fido, in the public park.
Or have a little chat with Joan
From any public telephone.

When you see PRIVATE anywhere
It means that you're not welcome there.
Better not peek at this or that—
"Curiosity killed the cat."

PLEASE DON'T FEED THE ANIMALS

Lollipops make the lion sick
(He eats the paper *and* the stick).

Peanuts were never meant for seals,
They need raw cod and wiggly eels.

Zoo animals get tummy-ache
From candy bars and chocolate cake.

Their keeper knows what food they need
He'll let you watch them while they feed.

But keep your distance while you do—
They'd love to try a bite of *you!*

Then *you* would be a sorry sight—
And *they* would lose their appetite.

NO LITTERING

The Litter Bug
Drops bits and scraps,
Paper and peel
And bottle caps.
He just pretends
He does not see
The trash can used
By you and me.

Perhaps what we should really do
Is throw *him* in the trash can, too!

DANGER

When it says DANGER on the pond
Don't even dream of sliding,
Don't try to test it with your toe,
The ice might crack—and in you'd go.
(How very silly to be stuck
And end up like a frozen duck!)

When it says DANGER on the beach
Don't wade, or go in swimming.
The tide would take you out to sea
And think how scary that would be.
(Before you found a rock to park
You might be gobbled by a shark!)

A danger sign is like a shout—

HANDS OFF!
TAKE CARE!
STAND BACK!
KEEP OUT!

QUIET! READING ROOM

Jennifer is scary-pale
As she reads a witch's tale.
Greg and Phil, this afternoon,
Are learning how to reach the moon.
Peter's eyes are popping out—
Whatever is his book about?

If your tongue wags all the time,
If you push, or bump, or climb,
Wiggle,
Giggle,
Sneeze and such,
You'll disturb them very much.

Sit down softly. Do not rush.
Shush.

Keep out

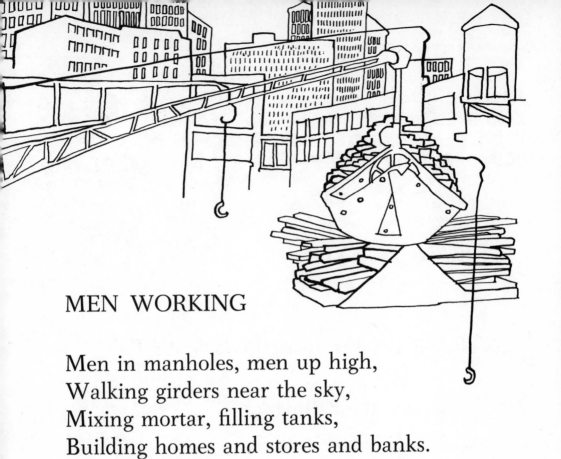

MEN WORKING

Men in manholes, men up high,
Walking girders near the sky,
Mixing mortar, filling tanks,
Building homes and stores and banks.

Ropes may tangle, glass may fly,
Bricks come tumbling from the sky!
There is danger all about—
Keep your poky-noses OUT.

ENTRANCE—EXIT

ENTRANCE signs mean THIS WAY IN

to the ball park,
to the zoo,
to the airport with the jets
(let's fly off to far Peru!)

EXIT signs mean THIS WAY OUT

    from the ball park,
from the zoo,
from the airport (can you guess
what we bought in far Peru?)

HOSPITAL ZONE

Carry skates
And walk your scooter,
Ring no bike bell,
Sound no hooter!
Here are grown-ups,
Girls and boys,
Much too sick
To bear such noise.

Remember how you felt when *you*
Were in the dumps
                with mumps
                or flu?

So please go quietly on your way
And find some other place to play.

KEEP OFF THE GRASS

This sign is standing here to show
That grass is trying hard to grow.
Mice may creep out on velvet feet
And birds hop round for worms to eat,
But please KEEP OFF, you girls and boys
With wagons, trucks, and heavy toys.
Don't stride about like Puss-in-Boots,
Trampling the tender little shoots.

When you were born, so weak and new,
Nobody ever trod on *you!*

WATCH YOUR STEP

Grab the rail on escalators!
Face the front in elevators!
On the platform, stand way back!
A train might come and hit you *smack!*

Someday you will fall down flop
If you always skip-and-hop.
Watch your step, like people do—
You are *not* a kangaroo.

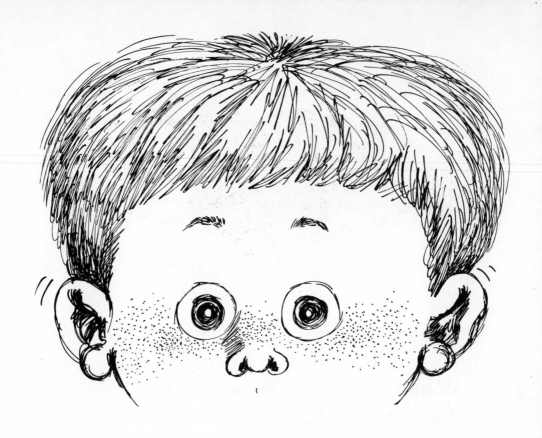

If you use your two bright eyes
Lots of signs you'll recognize.

Guides and guards, they stand about
To keep you safe, indoors and out.

And if you know the signs by heart
That's a sign you're really smart!

WATCH OUT!